A Christmas Carol Activity Book

By David Eastman

Illustrated by Monika Popowitz

Watermill Press

10 9 8 7 6 5 4 3

Complete the sentence by filling in the correct letters.

There was no doubt about it: Jacob Marley was as

___ ___ ___ ___
2   3   1   2

___ ___ ___
1   9   1

___ ___ ___ ___ ___ ___ ___ ___ .
2   7   7   8   6   1   4   5

1 = A	4 = I	7 = O
2 = D	5 = L	8 = R
3 = E	6 = N	9 = S

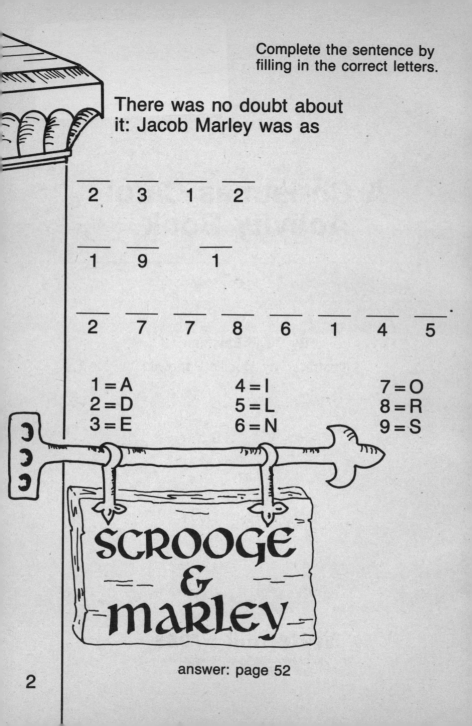

SCROOGE & MARLEY

answer: page 52

One Christmas Eve, Marley's partner sat in his counting house.

To find out Marley's partner's full name, solve each problem below. Then write the letter that matches each number.

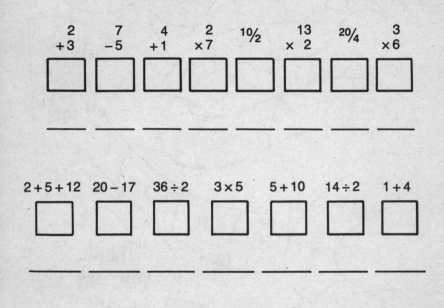

$$\begin{array}{c} 2 \\ +3 \end{array} \qquad \begin{array}{c} 7 \\ -5 \end{array} \qquad \begin{array}{c} 4 \\ +1 \end{array} \qquad \begin{array}{c} 2 \\ \times 7 \end{array} \qquad 10/2 \qquad \begin{array}{c} 13 \\ \times 2 \end{array} \qquad 20/4 \qquad \begin{array}{c} 3 \\ \times 6 \end{array}$$

___ ___ ___ ___ ___ ___ ___ ___

$$2+5+12 \qquad 20-17 \qquad 36 \div 2 \qquad 3 \times 5 \qquad 5+10 \qquad 14 \div 2 \qquad 1+4$$

___ ___ ___ ___ ___ ___ ___

2 = B	7 = G	18 = R
3 = C	14 = N	19 = S
5 = E	15 = O	26 = Z

answer: page 52

3

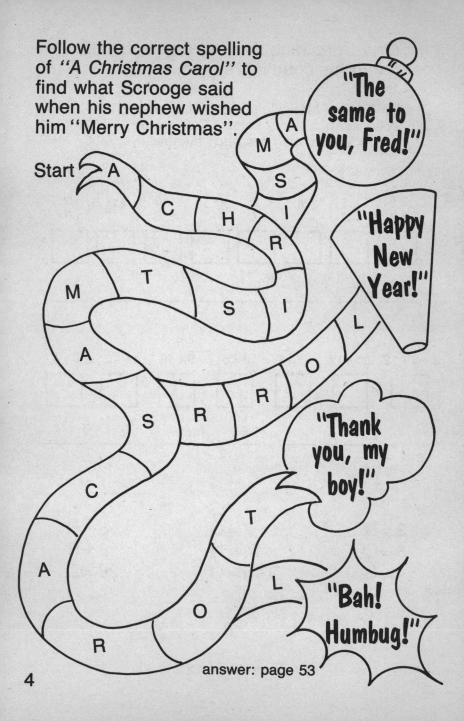

Two men came into Scrooge's shop and asked him for money to help the

___ ___ ___ ___ and the

___ ___ ___ ___ ___ ___ ___ ___ because they had nowhere to go on Christmas day.

Unscramble the letters below to spell the missing words.

ROPO

LOSHEEMS

answer: page 53

Scrooge looked at the men and asked, "Are there no prisons? Are there no workhouses?"

Can you fit the underlined words above into the puzzle below?

One of the men explained,

"

_____
mnay

_____
ant'c

_____
og

_____,
htree

_____
nad

_____
yamn

_____
dwolu

_____
herrat

_____."
ide

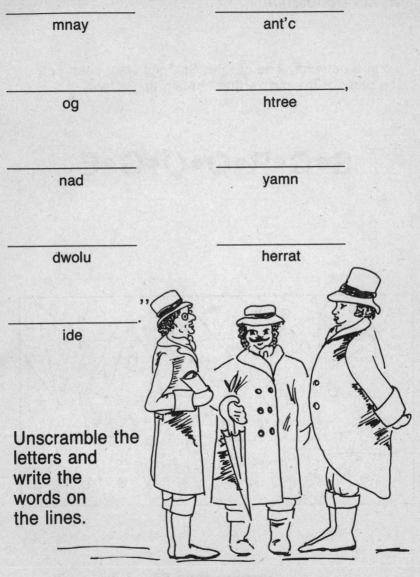

Unscramble the letters and write the words on the lines.

answer: page 53

7

"If they would rather die," snapped Scrooge, "then they had better do it, and decrease the surplus population!"

To find out what kind of man Scrooge was, color only the parts of the puzzle that contain the letters

S•C•R•O•O•G•E

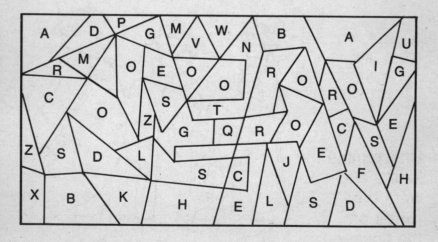

answer: page 54

Scrooge's clerk was a man named Bob

__ __ __ __ __ __ __ __ __

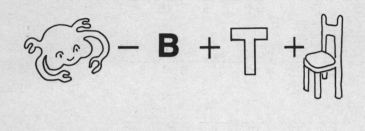

− AIR + it

Can you solve
the rebus to
find out what
the clerk's
name was?

answer: page 54

9

When it was time to close, Scrooge said to his clerk, "I suppose you'll want the day off tomorrow."

Use the code below to see what else he said.

" $\overline{}$ $\overline{}$ $\overline{}$ $\overline{}$ $\overline{}$ $\overline{}$
2   5   8   5   18   5

$\overline{}$ $\overline{}$ $\overline{}$ $\overline{}$ $\overline{}$ $\overline{}$
1   12   12   20   8   5

$\overline{}$ $\overline{}$ $\overline{}$ $\overline{}$ $\overline{}$ $\overline{}$ $\overline{}$
5   1   18   12   9   5   18

$\overline{}$ $\overline{}$ $\overline{}$ $\overline{}$ $\overline{}$ $\overline{}$ $\overline{}$
20   8   5   14   5   24   20

"

$\overline{}$ $\overline{}$ $\overline{}$.
4   1   25

A	B	C	D	E	F	G	H	I	J	K	L	M
1	2	3	4	5	6	7	8	9	10	11	12	13

N	O	P	Q	R	S	T	U	V	W	X	Y	Z
14	15	16	17	18	19	20	21	22	23	24	25	26

answer: page 54

Scrooge closed the office and went home.
For a moment he thought the knocker on
his door looked like someone he knew.

To find out who, write the answer to the clues, then read
down the circled letters.

1. ⃝_ bells ⃝ _ _ _ _ _
2. She sits on
   the tree top. ⃝ _ _ _ _
3. _ roasting
   on an open fire ⃝ _ _ _ _ _ _ _
4. _ the river and
   through the woods ⃝ _ . _ _ _
5. They ring on
   Christmas morning ⃝ _ _ _ _

6. You kiss under it ⃝ _ _ _ _ _ _ _ _
7. _ New Year! _ ⃝ _ _ _
8. Santa has 8 ⃝ _ _ _ _ _
9. Deck the
   Halls with this _ _ ⃝ _ _
10. Gift _ _ ⃝ _ _ _
11. 'Tis the
    season to be _ _ _ _ _ ⃝

<answer: page 54

11

In his bedroom, Scrooge was visited by Marley's ghost.

Fill in the correct vowels to find out what the ghost said.

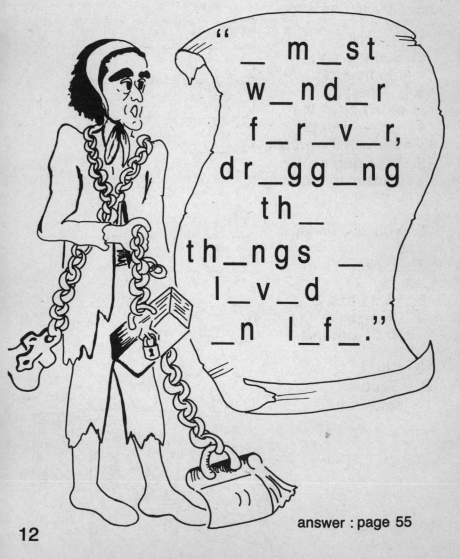

" _ m _ st w _ nd _ r f _ r _ v _ r, dr _ gg _ ng th _ th _ ngs _ l _ v _ d _ n l _ f _ . "

answer : page 55

12

"You can escape my fate.
You will be haunted by
three spirits. Heed them
well," added Marley's ghost.
Then he disappeared out the
window.

To find out what time the
first spirit was going to arrive,
solve this problem.

$$3 \times 4 \times 2 \div 6 \times 5 \div 10 + 3 - 2 + 10 - 1 =$$

Write the
answer here.

answer: page 55

The first spirit was the Ghost of Christmas Past.

Follow the path through the maze to find out what she showed Scrooge.

START

The place where Scrooge lived as a boy

A churchyard

The city hospital

A huge office building

A circus tent

The place where Scrooge went to school

The place where Scrooge met Bob Cratchit

The place where Jacob Marley was born

The Christmas party at Fezziwig's warehouse

The home of Scrooge's former girlfriend

FINISH

answer: page 55

The spirit said to Scrooge,

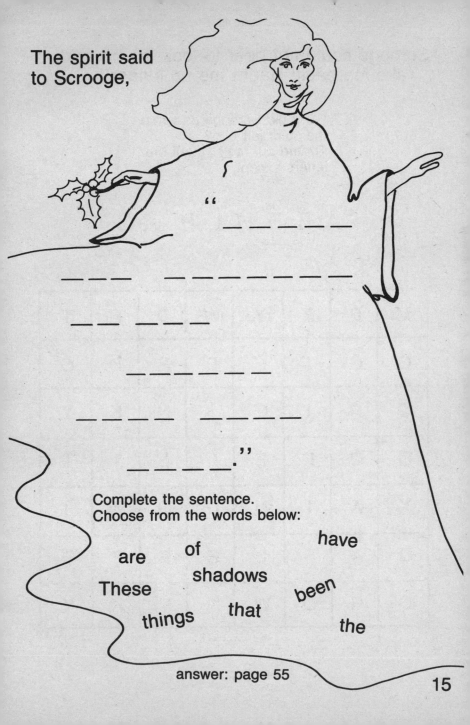

" _ _ _ _ _ _

_ _ _ _ _ _ _ _ _ _

_ _ _ _ _

_ _ _ _ _ _

_ _ _ _ _ _ _ _

_ _ _ _."

Complete the sentence.
Choose from the words below:

are   of   have

These   shadows

things   that   been

the

answer: page 55

Scrooge could not bear to look, so he said,
"Take me back! Haunt me no longer!"

What did Scrooge do when
the spirit left him?
To find out, color in all the
letters except

A E F H L P and S

M	B	Z	Y	W	D	R	T
O	G	I	H	E	R	D	O
C	R	I	M	I	N	K	Y
Q	O	F	E	L	L	I	T
X	W	I	N	D	O	W	J
G	A	S	L	E	E	P	O
C	R	O	W	N	V	K	Y

16

answer: page 56

The second spirit was the Ghost of Christmas Present.

Can you find these words in the puzzle?

I	G	I	G
T	H	N	V
H	O	L	L	Y
S	S	R	I	H
A	T	Y	C	T
Y	O	A	O	H
J	E	A	R	U
P	R	E	S	E	N	T

each   lit
ear   present
ghost   say
holly   song
ivy   stare
joy   torch
you

answer: page 56

17

When Scrooge touched the spirit's robe, he found he was floating through the streets on Christmas morning.

Trace their path by following the alphabet.

START

answer: page 56

18

The Cratchits ate these things on Christmas day:

goose
gravy
potatoes
applesauce
pudding
apples
oranges
chestnuts

Can you fit them all into the puzzle?

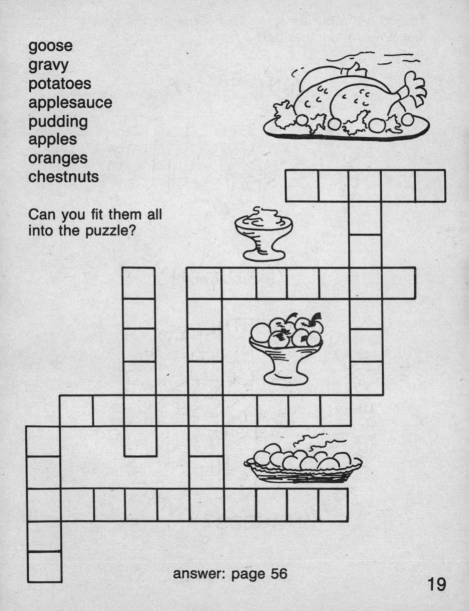

answer: page 56

19

Scrooge asked the spirit if Bob Cratchit's crippled son, Tiny Tim, would live.

To find out what the spirit said, separate the words that are run together below.

ISEEAVACANTSEATINTHECORNERANDACRUTCHWITHOUTANOWNER

THECHILDWILLDIEIFTHESESHADOWSREMAINUNALTEREDBYTHEFUTURE

answer: page 57

Scrooge heard Bob Cratchit propose a toast to "Mr. Scrooge, the founder of the feast." Mrs. Cratchit replied, "The founder of the feast indeed! I wish I had him here. I'd give him . . ."

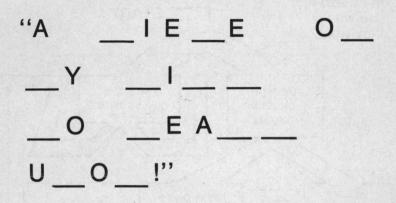

"A __ I E __ E   O __

__ Y   __ I __ __

__ O   __ E A __ __

U __ O __ !"

To find out what she would give, write the correct consonants on the lines. Choose from the ones in the circle.

C D
F F M M
N N P P
S T T

answer: page 57

The Ghost of Christmas Present took Scrooge to many places, and everywhere they went, people were filled with joy as they wished each other Merry Christmas.

Follow the path through the maze to see where they went.

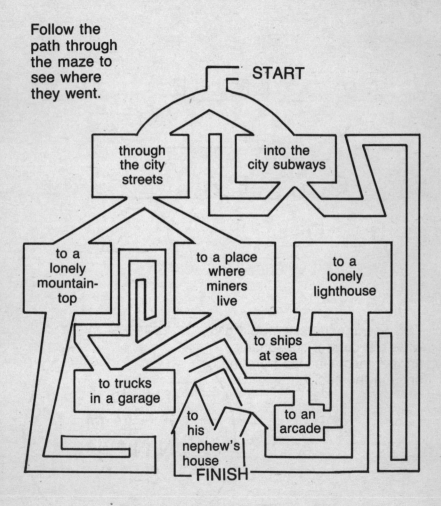

START

through the city streets

into the city subways

to a lonely mountain-top

to a place where miners live

to a lonely lighthouse

to ships at sea

to trucks in a garage

to his nephew's house

to an arcade

FINISH

answer: page 57

Scrooge's nephew and friends played games on Christmas day as Scrooge and the Ghost of Christmas Present looked on.

Use the code to find out what games they played.

1.
$\overline{S}\ \overline{B}\ \overline{E}\ \overline{S}\ \overline{R}\ \overline{V}\ \overline{G}\ \overline{F}$

2.
$\overline{O}\ \overline{Y}\ \overline{V}\ \overline{A}\ \overline{Q}\ \overline{Z}\ \overline{N}\ \overline{A}\ \overline{F}$,

$\overline{O}\ \overline{H}\ \overline{S}\ \overline{S}$.

3.
$\overline{U}\ \overline{B}\ \overline{J}$, $\overline{J}\ \overline{U}\ \overline{R}\ \overline{A}$,

$\overline{N}\ \overline{A}\ \overline{Q}$ $\overline{J}\ \overline{U}\ \overline{R}\ \overline{E}\ \overline{R}$

4.
$\overline{L}\ \overline{R}\ \overline{F}$ $\overline{N}\ \overline{A}\ \overline{Q}$ $\overline{A}\ \overline{B}$

| A = N |
| B = O |
| C = P |
| D = Q |
| E = R |
| F = S |
| G = T |
| H = U |
| I = V |
| J = W |
| K = X |
| L = Y |
| M = Z |

answer: page 57

Later, the spirit introduced Scrooge to two ragged, miserable children. "They belong to all mankind," said the spirit. "Beware of them both."

To find out what they were called, hold this page up to a mirror.

"The boy is "Ignorance."
The girl is "Want."

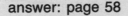

24

answer: page 58

"Oh, Spirit," said Scrooge, when he heard that the children were doomed. "Is there no place they can go?"

To find out the spirit's reply, circle the odd boxes in the odd-numbered rows and the even boxes in the even-numbered rows.

1	A	B	R	C	E	D	T	F	H	G	E
2	J	R	L	E	M	N	Q	O	V	P	X
3	R	Y	I	Z	S	!	O	A	N	B	S
4	C	?	D	A	F	R	G	E	J	T	L
5	H	M	E	Q	R	V	E	X	N	Y	O
6	Z	W	!	O	B	R	C	K	D	H	F
7	O	G	U	J	S	L	E	M	S	Q	?

Then write the circled letters or punctuation marks on the lines below.

— — —   — — — — —   — —

— — — — — — —   — — —

— — — — —   — —

— — — — — — — — —

answer: page 58

The Ghost of Christmas Present
had grown very old.
Suddenly Scrooge realized
that he was gone.

To find out what
time it was, draw the
hands on the clock.
The minute hand
should point to the
number that is the
answer to this
problem:

$$8 \times 8 \div 16 \times 5 \div 4 - 2 + 9 =$$

———

The hour hand should
point to the number
that is the answer
to this problem:

$$6 \times 7 \div 2 \div 3 \times 2 - 2 =$$

———

answer: page 58

The last of the three spirits . . . the Ghost of
Christmas Yet to Come . . . was a phantom
who wore a hooded robe that covered

$\overline{}$ $\overline{}$ $\overline{}$ $\overline{}$ $\overline{}$ $\overline{}$ $\overline{}$ $\overline{}$ $\overline{}$ $\overline{}$
F W F S Z U I J O H

$\overline{}$ $\overline{}$ $\overline{}$ $\overline{}$ $\overline{}$ $\overline{}$ $\overline{}$ $\overline{}$ $\overline{}$
F Y D F Q U   P O F

$\overline{}$ $\overline{}$ $\overline{}$ $\overline{}$ $\overline{}$ $\overline{}$ $\overline{}$ $\overline{}$ $\overline{}$ $\overline{}$ $\overline{}$ $\overline{}$
P V U T U S F U D I F E

$\overline{}$ $\overline{}$ $\overline{}$ $\overline{}$.
I B O E

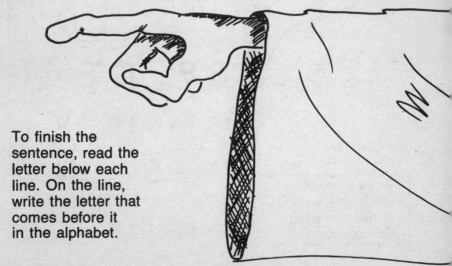

To finish the
sentence, read the
letter below each
line. On the line,
write the letter that
comes before it
in the alphabet.

answer: page 58

When he saw the Ghost of Christmas Yet to Come, Scrooge said,

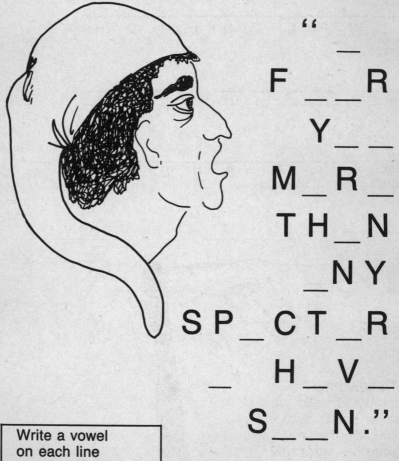

"
F _ _ R
Y _ _
M _ R _
TH _ N
_ N Y
SP _ CT _ R
_ H _ V _
S _ _ N."

Write a vowel
on each line
to find out what
Scrooge said.

answer: page 59

As the phantom led him through the city, Scrooge learned that

— — — — — — —

— — —   — — — — .

To complete the sentence above, write the opposite of each word in the spaces below. Then write the circled letters on the lines above.

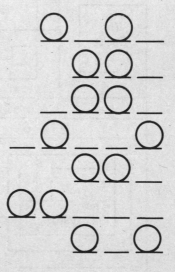

FAST

WOMEN

SOME

LIFE

SUBTRACT

CLEAN

BEGINNING

answer: page 59

The phantom led Scrooge deep into the city.

To find out where they went, find the path through the maze.

answer: page 59

They entered a shop where things of all kinds were bought and sold.

Hidden in the puzzle are the names of ten things they saw in the shop. Find and circle them.

B	O	N	E	S	M	A
O	F	K	E	Y	S	S
T	R	I	P	E	T	C
T	R	Y	L	H	O	H
L	U	A	G	E	N	A
E	C	I	G	O	S	I
S	E	Y	R	S	Z	N
W	H	I	N	G	E	S

OLD JOE'S
BUY AND SELL MOST
- ANYTHING -

answer: page 59

Three people came into the shop to sell things they had taken from the man who had died. They were a laundress, an undertaker's man, and a cleaning woman or

__ __ __ __ __ __ __ __ __
1   2   3   4   5   6   7   8   9

Read the clues, write the answers on the lines. Then write the circled letters on the correct spaces above.

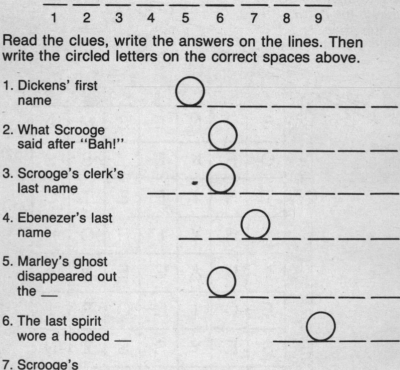

1. Dickens' first name

2. What Scrooge said after "Bah!"

3. Scrooge's clerk's last name

4. Ebenezer's last name

5. Marley's ghost disappeared out the __

6. The last spirit wore a hooded __

7. Scrooge's partner's last name

8. Scrooge's partner's first name

9. He used a crutch

answer: page 60

32

Using the clues below, can you figure out who sold what?

1. The two women entered one after the other.
2. The person who entered first sold her goods last.
3. Mrs. Dilber sold sheets and towels.
4. The laundress sold her things first.
5. Bedcurtains and blankets were sold last.
6. Someone sold a pencil case and a brooch.

Draw lines to connect each person with the goods he or she sold.

undertaker's man   sheets and towels

cleaning woman   bedcurtains and blankets

laundress   pencil case and brooch

What was Mrs. Dilber's occupation?

_____

answer: page 60

The cleaning woman laughed and said, "He frightened everyone away from him when he was alive, to profit us when he was dead! Ha, ha, ha!" .

Scrooge turned to the Ghost of Christmas Yet to Come, and said,

"I _ __ _ y o n _

_ e e l _ __ _ o t i __ _

__ u s e d   b y   t ___

__ n's   d _ __ h,

s ___   t ___

p ___ o n   __

_ e."

answer: page 60

But the only emotion the ghost could show Scrooge was

1	2	3	4	5	6	7	8
L	P	A	E	U	S	E	R

To find out what that emotion was, move each odd-numbered letter to the next higher numbered space, and move each even-numbered letter to the next lower numbered space.

answer: page 60

"Let me see some tenderness connected with a death," said Scrooge. And so the phantom took him to Bob Cratchit's house, where he learned that

‾‾‾‾‾‾‾ ‾‾‾‾‾‾ ‾‾‾‾‾‾ ‾‾‾‾‾‾ .
I T Y N   I M T .   A D H   I D E D

Unscramble the letters and write the words on the lines.

Following the Ghost of Christmas Yet to Come, Scrooge passed his office and looked in the window.

Write the correct vowels on the lines to find out what he saw.

S _ m _ _ n _

_ l s _ w _ s

_ n h _ s

c h _ _ r.

answer: page 61

As they arrived at a graveyard, Scrooge asked the phantom, "Are these the shadows of things that *will* be, or

—— —— ——   —— —— —— ——
1   18 5   20 8   5 25

—— —— —— —— —— —— ——   —— ——
19 8   1   4 15 23 19   15 6

—— —— —— —— —— ——   —— —— —— ——
20 8   9 14 7 19   20 8   1 20

? "

—— —— ——   —— ——
13 1 25   2   5

Find each number on the wheel. Write the correct letter on the line.

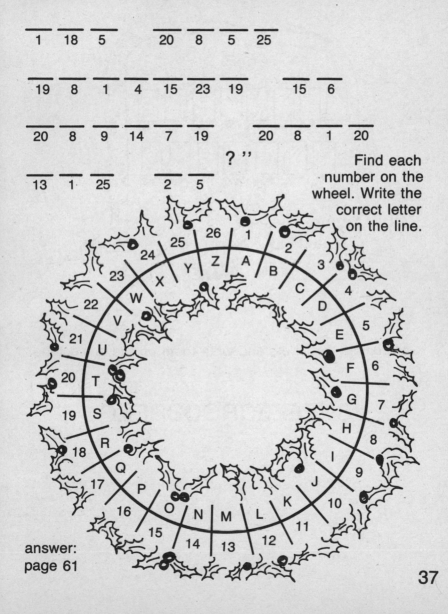

answer:
page 61

The phantom did not answer, but pointed to a grave. What name was on the grave?

Unscramble the letters and write them on the gravestone.

SNEEZECROOBREEG

answer: page 61

Scrooge fell to his <u>knees</u> with this <u>plea</u>: "Tell me I can <u>change</u> these <u>shadows</u> by changing my life! I will <u>honor</u> <u>Christmas</u> in my <u>heart</u> and try to <u>keep</u> it all the <u>year</u>."

Can you fit the underlined words into the puzzle below?

answer: page 61

Scrooge seized the phantom's hand, but the spirit pulled away. Then something happened to the phantom.

Use the code to find out what happened.

$\overline{6}$ $\overline{12}$ $\quad$ $\overline{3}$ $\overline{9}$ $\overline{7}$ $\overline{7}$ $\overline{1}$ $\overline{10}$ $\overline{11}$ $\overline{5}$ $\overline{4}$

$\overline{1}$ $\overline{8}$ $\overline{4}$ $\quad$ $\overline{4}$ $\overline{13}$ $\overline{6}$ $\overline{8}$ $\overline{4}$ $\overline{7}$ $\overline{5}$ $\overline{4}$

$\overline{4}$ $\overline{9}$ $\overline{13}$ $\overline{8}$ $\quad$ $\overline{6}$ $\overline{8}$ $\overline{12}$ $\overline{9}$

$\overline{1}$ $\quad$ $\overline{2}$ $\overline{5}$ $\overline{4}$ $\overline{10}$ $\overline{9}$ $\overline{11}$ $\overline{12}$

1 = A	8 = N
2 = B	9 = O
3 = C	10 = P
4 = D	11 = S
5 = E	12 = T
6 = I	13 = W
7 = L	

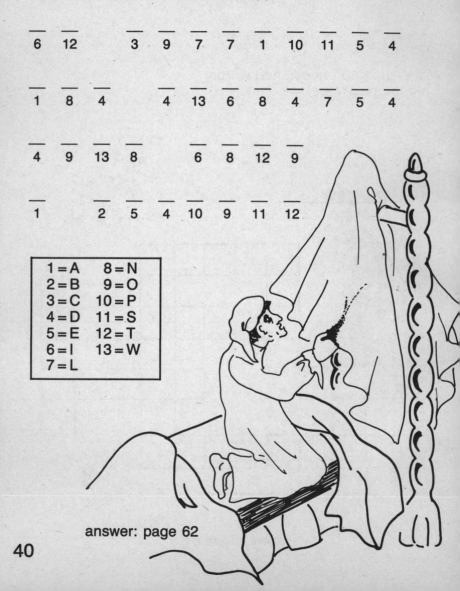

answer: page 62

40

Scrooge realized he was in his own room.
He scrambled out of bed, laughing and
crying at the same time.

Can you find all the above words hidden
in the puzzle below?

S	C	R	O	O	G	E	H
C	L	R	A	N	D	E	I
R	A	E	Y	T	M	T	S
A	U	A	M	I	N	H	B
M	G	L	T	B	N	E	E
B	H	I	W	H	M	G	D
L	I	Z	A	A	E	X	O
E	N	E	S	W	S	F	W
D	G	D	R	O	O	M	N
L	A	O	U	T	C	R	Y

answer: page 62

41

As Scrooge ran around his room, he said he felt as light as a feather, as happy as an angel, and as merry as a schoolboy.

Schoolboy is a compound word—it is made up of two words. How many compound words can you make by drawing lines from a word in column A to a word in column B?

A	B
	body
any	brush
	cover
butter	fly
	milk
every	one
	paper
news	stand
	thing
no	water
	wear
some	where
under	

answer: page 62

He did not know how long he had been with the spirits, so he did not know

———————— ————————
THAW   YAD

———————— ————————.
TI   SAW

Unscramble the letters and put the correct words on the lines.

answer: page 62

Scrooge put his head out the window.

1	A	G	B	O	C	L	D	D	E
2	E	F	N	G	S	H	U	I	N
3	J	L	K	I	L	G	M	H	N
4	T	O	;	P	H	Q	E	R	A
5	S	V	T	E	U	N	V	L	W
6	Y	X	S	Y	K	Z	Y	A	;
7	B	S	C	W	D	E	E	E	F
8	T	G	,	H	F	I	R	J	E
9	K	S	L	H	M	A	N	I	O
10	R	P	A	Q	N	R	D	S	M
11	T	E	U	R	V	R	W	Y	Y
12	B	Y	E	Z	L	A	L	B	S

To find out what he saw and heard, cross out the odd boxes in the odd-numbered rows and the even boxes in the even-numbered rows. Then write the remaining letters and punctuation marks on the lines.

_ _ _ _ _ _ _ _ _ _ _

_ _ _ _ _ _ _ _ _ _

_ _ _ _ _ _ _ _ _

_ _ _ _ _ _ _ _ .

answer: page 63

"What's today?" cried Scrooge. And a boy in the street below replied,

"
$\overline{}$ $\overline{}$ $\overline{}$,
$\overline{5}$ $\overline{9}$ $\overline{8}$

$\overline{2}$ $\overline{4}$ $\overline{7}$ $\overline{5}$ $\overline{8}$ $\overline{9}$ $\overline{6}$ $\overline{1}$ $\overline{8}$

!"
$\overline{3}$ $\overline{1}$ $\overline{10}$

1 = A
2 = C
3 = D
4 = H
5 = I
6 = M
7 = R
8 = S
9 = T
10 = Y

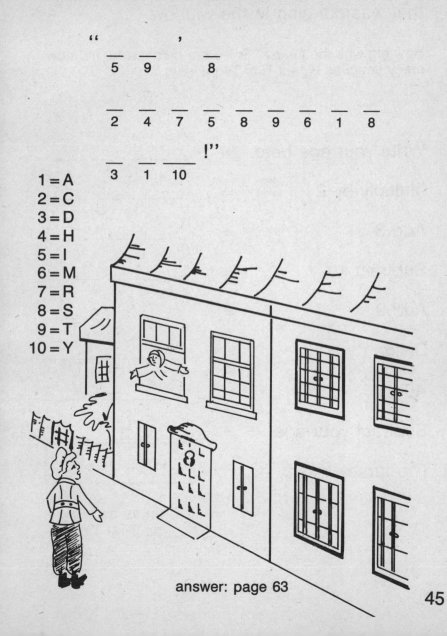

answer: page 63

Scrooge told the boy to go to the poultry shop on the next street and buy the turkey that was hanging in the window.

How big was the turkey? Solve the problem to find how many times as big as Tiny Tim it was.

Write your age here ▶ _____

Multiply by 2 = _____

Add 3 = _____

Subtract 10 = _____

Add 9 = _____

Divide by 2 = _____

Add 1 = _____

Subtract your age = _____

The turkey was

⬚

times as big
as Tiny Tim

answer: page 63

What did Scrooge do with the turkey?

Draw a line to show what he did. Solve each problem and take the path with the correct answer.

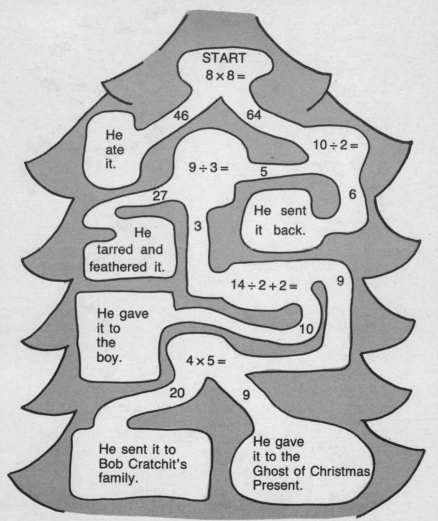

START

$8 \times 8 =$

46   64

He ate it.

$10 \div 2 =$

$9 \div 3 =$ 5

27   6

3   He sent it back.

He tarred and feathered it.

$14 \div 2 + 2 =$ 9

He gave it to the boy.

10

$4 \times 5 =$

20   9

He sent it to Bob Cratchit's family.

He gave it to the Ghost of Christmas Present.

answer: page 63

Scrooge went to church, then walked through the streets, and everything he saw brought him pleasure. In the afternoon, he turned his steps

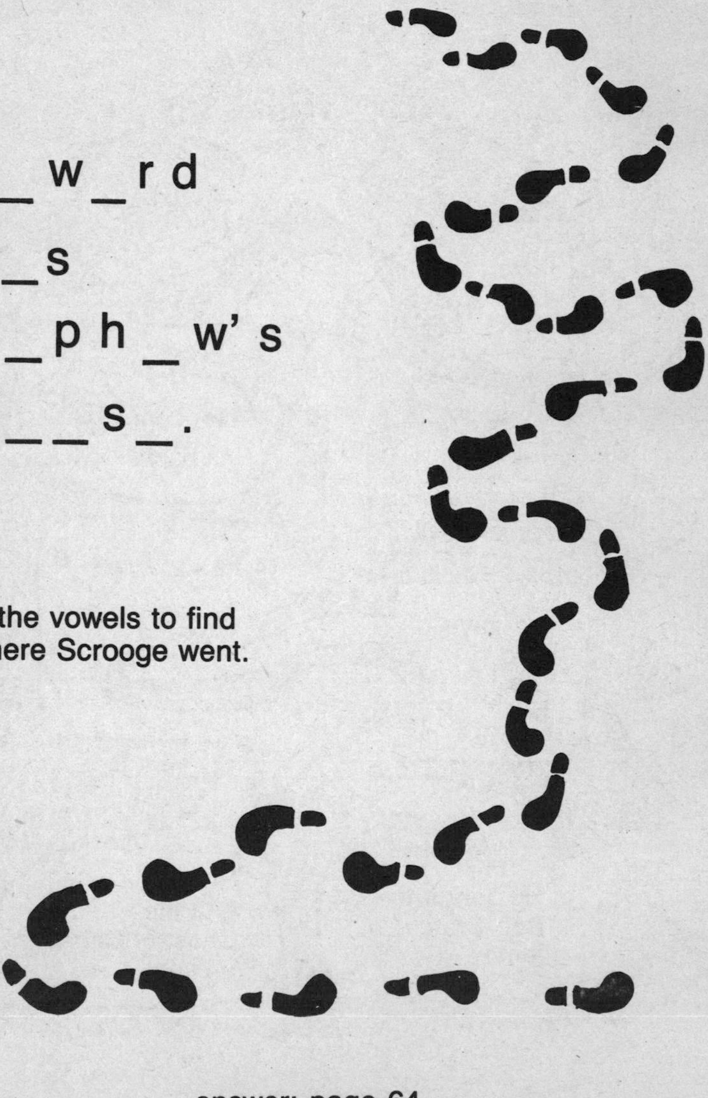

t _ w _ r d

h _ s

n _ p h _ w' s

h _ _ s _ .

Fill in the vowels to find out where Scrooge went.

answer: page 64

He passed the door many times before he finally had the courage to knock.

Unscramble the letters to find out how many times he passed the door.

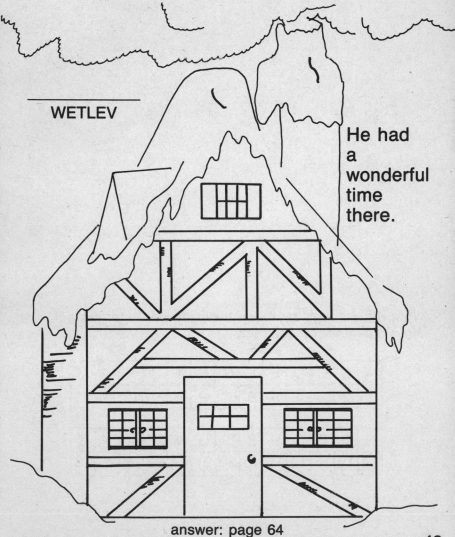

_____
WETLEV

He had a wonderful time there.

answer: page 64

The next morning, Bob Cratchit came to work late. "I'm not going to stand for this," growled Scrooge. "Therefore . . .

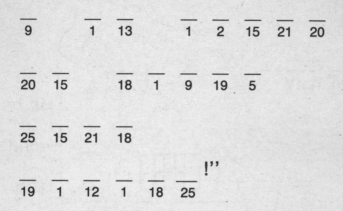

$\overline{9}$ $\overline{1}$ $\overline{13}$ $\overline{1}$ $\overline{2}$ $\overline{15}$ $\overline{21}$ $\overline{20}$

$\overline{20}$ $\overline{15}$ $\overline{18}$ $\overline{1}$ $\overline{9}$ $\overline{19}$ $\overline{5}$

$\overline{25}$ $\overline{15}$ $\overline{21}$ $\overline{18}$

$\overline{19}$ $\overline{1}$ $\overline{12}$ $\overline{1}$ $\overline{18}$ $\overline{25}$!"

What did Scrooge say? Use the code below to find out. Write one letter on each line.

A	B	C	D	E	F	G	H	I	J	K	L	M
1	2	3	4	5	6	7	8	9	10	11	12	13

N	O	P	Q	R	S	T	U	V	W	X	Y	Z
14	15	16	17	18	19	20	21	22	23	24	25	26

answer: page 64

50

And Scrooge did just what he said! He became like a father to Tiny Tim, who did *NOT* die, and he became a good man. And it was always said of him that

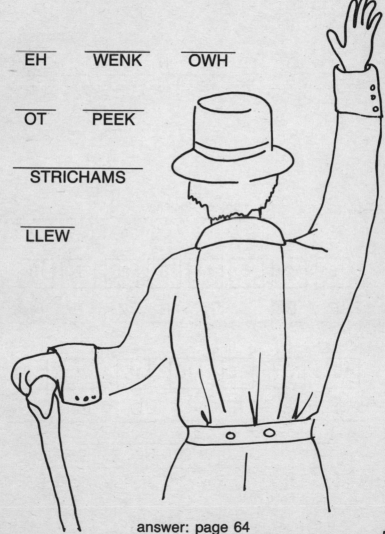

EH   WENK   OWH

OT   PEEK

STRICHAMS

LLEW

answer: page 64

answer for page 2

$$\frac{D}{2} \quad \frac{E}{3} \quad \frac{A}{1} \quad \frac{D}{2}$$

$$\frac{A}{1} \quad \frac{S}{9} \quad \frac{A}{1}$$

$$\frac{D}{2} \quad \frac{O}{7} \quad \frac{O}{7} \quad \frac{R}{8} \quad \frac{N}{6} \quad \frac{A}{1} \quad \frac{I}{4} \quad \frac{L}{5}.$$

answer for page 3

5	2	5	14	5	26	5	18
E	B	E	N	E	Z	E	R

19	3	18	15	15	7	5
S	C	R	O	O	G	E

52

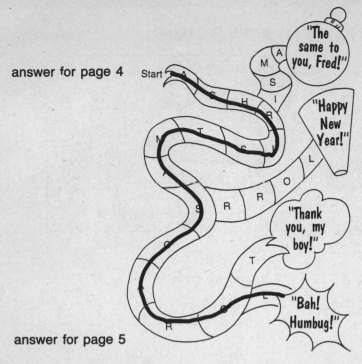

answer for page 4

Start

"The same to you, Fred!"

"Happy New Year!"

"Thank you, my boy!"

"Bah! Humbug!"

answer for page 5

P O O R

H O M E L E S S

answer for page 6

					T	
A		W			H	
S	C	R	O	O	G	E
K		R			R	
E		K		M	E	N
D		H			O	
	L	O	O	K	E	D
		U				
P	R	I	S	O	N	S
		E				
		S				

answer for page 7

"

___many___
mnay

___can't___
ant'c

___go___
og

___there___
htree

___and___
nad

___many___
yamn

___would___
dwolu

___rather___
herrat

___die___
ide

"

53

answer for page 8

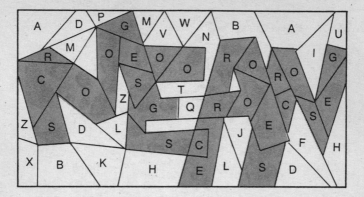

answer for page 9

C R A T C H I T

answer for page 10

" B E   H E R E
  2 5   8 5 18 5

A L L   T H E
1 12 12   20 8 5

E A R L I E R
5 1 18 12 9 5 18

T H E   N E X T
20 8 5   14 5 24 20

D A Y "
4 1 25

answer for page 11

Ⓙ I N G L E

Ⓐ N G E L

Ⓒ H E S T N U T S

Ⓞ V E R

Ⓑ E L L S

Ⓜ I S T L E T O E

H Ⓐ P P Y

Ⓡ E I N D E E R

H O Ⓛ L Y

P R Ⓔ S E N T

J O L L Ⓨ

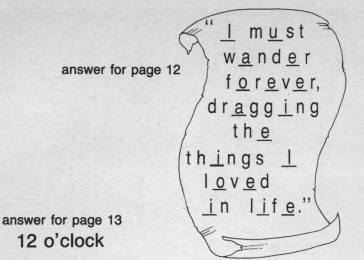

answer for page 12

" I must wander forever, dragging the things I loved in life."

answer for page 13

12 o'clock

answer for page 14

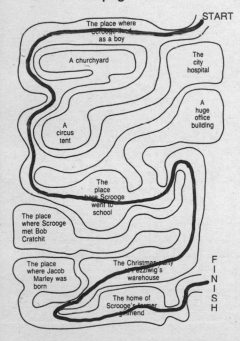

answer for page 15

" These are shadows of the things that have been."

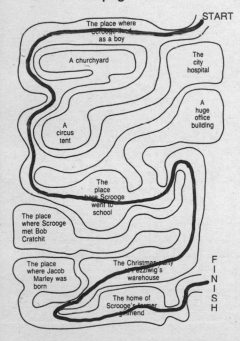

M	B	Z	Y	W	D	R	T
O	G	I	H	E	R	D	O
C	R	I	M	I	N	K	Y
Q	O	F	E	L	L	I	T
X	W	I	N	D	O	W	J
G	A	S	L	E	E	P	O
C	R	O	W	N	V	K	Y

I	G	I	G	
T	H	N	V	
H	O	L	L	Y
S	S	R	I	H
A	T	Y	C	T
Y	O	A	O	H
J	E	A	R	U

P	R	E	S	E	N	T

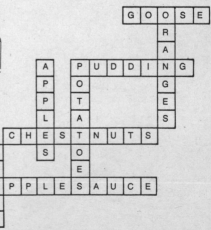

56

 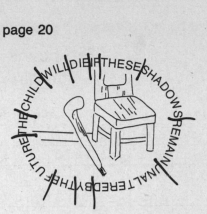

answer for page 21

"A P I E <u>C</u>E O F

<u>M</u>Y <u>M</u> I <u>N</u> <u>D</u>

<u>T</u> <u>O</u> <u>F</u> E A<u>S</u> T

U <u>P</u> <u>O</u> <u>N</u> !"

answer for page 22

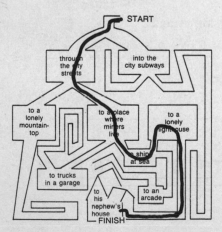

answer for page 23

1. <u>F</u> <u>O</u> <u>R</u> <u>F</u> <u>E</u> <u>I</u> <u>T</u> <u>S</u>
    S B E S R V G F

2. <u>B</u> <u>L</u> <u>I</u> <u>N</u> <u>D</u> <u>M</u> <u>A</u> <u>N</u>'<u>S</u>
    O Y V A Q Z N A F

   <u>B</u> <u>U</u> <u>F</u> <u>F</u> .
    O H S S

3. <u>H</u> <u>O</u> <u>W</u>, <u>W</u> <u>H</u> <u>E</u> <u>N</u>,
    U B J   J U R A

   <u>A</u> <u>N</u> <u>D</u> <u>W</u> <u>H</u> <u>E</u> <u>R</u> <u>E</u>
    N A Q   J U R E R

4. <u>Y</u> <u>E</u> <u>S</u> <u>A</u> <u>N</u> <u>D</u> <u>N</u> <u>O</u>
    L R F   N A Q   A B

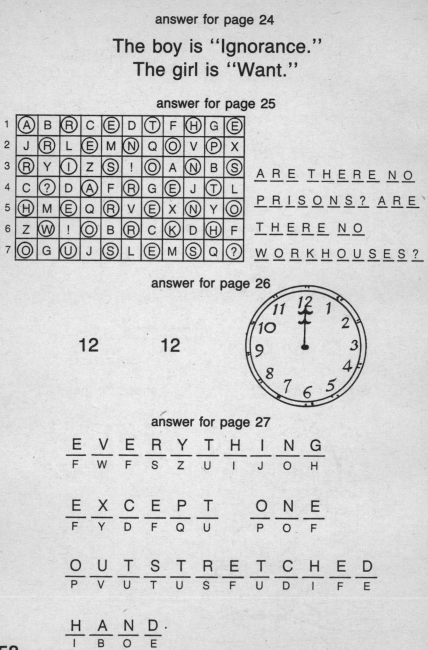

answer for page 24

The boy is "Ignorance."
The girl is "Want."

answer for page 25

	1	2	3	4	5	6	7	8	9	10
1	Ⓐ	B	Ⓡ	C	Ⓔ	D	Ⓣ	F	Ⓗ	G	Ⓔ
2	J	Ⓡ	L	Ⓔ	M	Ⓝ	Q	Ⓞ	V	Ⓟ	X
3	Ⓡ	Y	Ⓘ	Z	Ⓢ	!	Ⓞ	A	Ⓝ	B	Ⓢ
4	C	⓵	D	Ⓐ	F	Ⓡ	G	Ⓔ	J	Ⓣ	L
5	Ⓗ	M	Ⓔ	Q	Ⓡ	V	Ⓔ	X	Ⓝ	Y	Ⓞ
6	Z	Ⓦ	!	Ⓞ	B	Ⓡ	C	Ⓚ	D	Ⓗ	F
7	Ⓞ	G	Ⓤ	J	Ⓢ	L	Ⓔ	M	Ⓢ	Q	⓵

A R E   T H E R E   N O
P R I S O N S ?   A R E
T H E R E   N O
W O R K H O U S E S ?

answer for page 26

12   **12**

answer for page 27

E V E R Y T H I N G
F W F S Z U I J O H

E X C E P T   O N E
F Y D F Q U   P O F

O U T S T R E T C H E D
P V U T U S F U D I F E

H A N D .
I B O E

answer for page 28

"<u>I</u>
F<u>E</u><u>A</u>R
Y<u>OU</u>
M<u>O</u>R<u>E</u>
THA<u>N</u>
<u>A</u>NY
S P<u>E</u> CTE<u>R</u>
<u>I</u> HA<u>VE</u>
SE<u>E</u>N."

answer for page 29

<u>S O M E O N E</u>

<u>H A D</u>   <u>D I E D</u> .

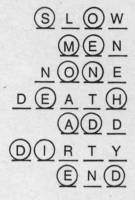

answer for page 30

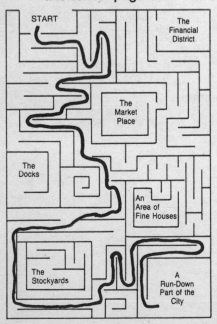

answer for page 31

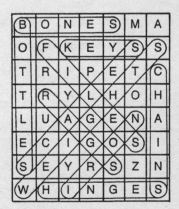

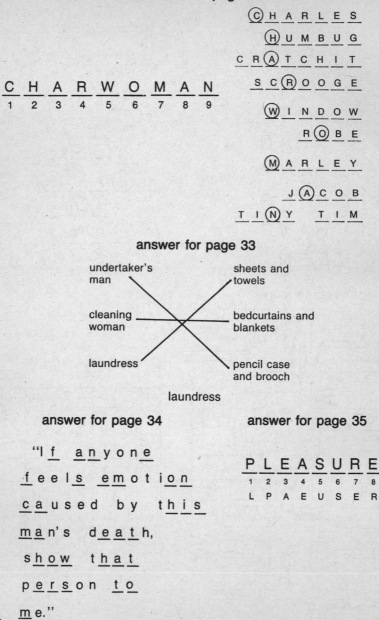

answer for page 32

C(C)H A R L E S
(H)U M B U G
C R(A)T C H I T
S C(R)O O G E

(W)I N D O W
R(O)B E

(M)A R L E Y

J(A)C O B
T I(N)Y   T I M

C H A R W O M A N
1 2 3 4 5 6 7 8 9

answer for page 33

undertaker's man — pencil case and brooch

cleaning woman — bedcurtains and blankets

laundress — sheets and towels

laundress

answer for page 34

"If anyone
feels emotion
caused by this
man's death,
show that
person to
me."

answer for page 35

P L E A S U R E
1 2 3 4 5 6 7 8
L P A E U S E R

60

T I N Y   T I M   H A D   D I E D.
I T Y N   I M T   A D H   I D E D

S _o_ m e _o_ n e

_e_ l s e _e_ w _a_ s

_i_ n   h _i_ s

c h _a_ i r.

A R E   T H E Y
1 18 5   20 8 5 25

S H A D O W S   O F
19 8 1 4 15 23 19   15 6

T H I N G S   T H A T
20 8 9 14 7 19   20 8 1 20

M A Y   B E ?"
13 1 25   2 5

E B E N E Z E R   S C R O O G E

answer for page 40

$\underline{I}_{6}$ $\underline{T}_{12}$ $\underline{C}_{3}$ $\underline{O}_{9}$ $\underline{L}_{7}$ $\underline{L}_{7}$ $\underline{A}_{1}$ $\underline{P}_{10}$ $\underline{S}_{11}$ $\underline{E}_{5}$ $\underline{D}_{4}$

$\underline{A}_{1}$ $\underline{N}_{8}$ $\underline{D}_{4}$ $\underline{D}_{4}$ $\underline{W}_{13}$ $\underline{I}_{6}$ $\underline{N}_{8}$ $\underline{D}_{4}$ $\underline{L}_{7}$ $\underline{E}_{5}$ $\underline{D}_{4}$

$\underline{D}_{4}$ $\underline{O}_{9}$ $\underline{W}_{13}$ $\underline{N}_{8}$ $\underline{I}_{6}$ $\underline{N}_{8}$ $\underline{T}_{12}$ $\underline{O}_{9}$

$\underline{A}_{1}$ $\underline{B}_{2}$ $\underline{E}_{5}$ $\underline{D}_{4}$ $\underline{P}_{10}$ $\underline{O}_{9}$ $\underline{S}_{11}$ $\underline{T}_{12}$

answer for page 41

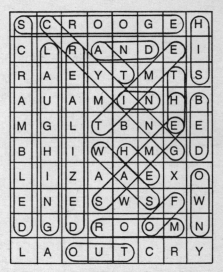

answer for page 42

A   B
any   body
butter   brush
            cover
every   fly
            milk
news   one
            paper
no   stand
some   thing
            water
under   wear
            where

answer for page 43

WHAT	DAY
THAW	YAD

IT	WAS
TI	SAW

62

answer for page 44

1	A	G	B	O	C	L	D	D	E
2	E	F	N	G	S	H	U	V	N
3	J	L	K	I	L	G	M	H	N
4	T	O	;	P	H	O	E	R	A
5	S	V	T	E	U	N	L	L	W
6	Y	X	S	Y	K	Z	Y	A	;
7	B	S	C	W	D	E	E	E	F
8	T	O	,	H	F	L	R	J	E
9	K	S	L	H	M	A	N	I	O
10	R	P	A	Q	N	P	D	S	M
11	T	E	U	R	Y	R	W	Y	Y
12	B	Y	E	Z	L	A	L	B	S

G O L D E N   S U N L I G H T ;

H E A V E N L Y   S K Y ;

S W E E T ,   F R E S H   A I R

A N D   M E R R Y   B E L L S .

answer for page 45

" I T ' S
  5 9   8

C H R I S T M A S
2 4 7 5 8 9 6 1 8

D A Y ! "
3 1 10

answer for page 46 is 2

answer for page 47

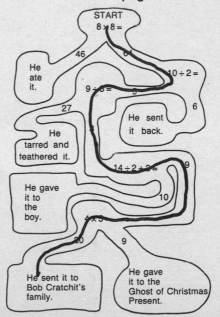

START
8 × 8 =

46
64
10 ÷ 2 =
He ate it.
9 ÷ 3 =
5
6
27
He sent it back.
He tarred and feathered it.
14 ÷ 2 + 2 =
9
He gave it to the boy.
10
4 × 5
20
9
He sent it to Bob Cratchit's family.
He gave it to the Ghost of Christmas Present.

answer for page 48

t <u>o</u> w <u>a</u> r d

h <u>i</u> s

n <u>e</u> p h <u>e</u> w's

h <u>o</u> u s <u>e</u>.

answer for page 49

TWELVE
———————
WETLEV

answer for page 50

I — A M — A B O U T
9 — 1 13 — 1 2 15 21 20

T O — R A I S E
20 15 — 18 1 9 19 5

Y O U R
25 15 21 18

S A L A R Y !"
19 1 12 1 18 25

answer for page 51

HE — KNEW — HOW
EH — WENK — OWH

TO — KEEP
OT — PEEK

CHRISTMAS
STRICHAMS

WELL
LLEW

64